How to use this book

Follow the advice, in italics, given for you on each page.
Support the children as they read the text that is shaded in cream.
Praise *the children at every step!*

Detailed guidance is provided in the Read Write Inc. Phonics Handbook

8 reading activities

Children:

- *Practise reading the speed sounds.*
- *Read the green and red words for the story.*
- *Listen as you read the introduction.*
- *Discuss the vocabulary check with you.*
- *Read the story.*
- *Re-read the story and discuss the 'questions to talk about'.*
- *Re-read the story with fluency and expression.*
- *Practise reading the speed words.*

Speed sounds

Consonants *Say the pure sounds (do not add 'uh').*

f (ff)	l ll (le)	m mm	n nn kn	r rr	s (ss)	v ve	' z zz s	sh	th	ng nk

b bb	c k ck	d dd	g gg	h	j	p pp	qu	t tt	w wh	x	y	ch tch

Vowels *Say the sounds in and out of order.*

at	hen head	in	on	up	day	see happy	high	blow

zoo	look	car	for door snore	fair	whirl	shout	boy

Each box contains one sound but sometimes more than one grapheme. Focus graphemes are **circled**.

Green words

l<u>ow</u>   s<u>low</u>   lo<u>ng</u>   t<u>igh</u>t   dre<u>ss</u>   litt<u>le</u>

t<u>oo</u>   t<u>oo</u>t   f<u>oo</u>d   b<u>oo</u>t   st<u>oo</u>l   <u>sh</u><u>oo</u>

c<u>off</u>`<u>ee</u>   →   c<u>off</u><u>ee</u>

Red words

old   my   <u>are</u>

5

Vocabulary check

Discuss the meaning (as used in the story) after the children have read each word.

	definition:
scooter	a two wheeled vehicle that you move by pushing your feet
cap	a hat with a peak

Punctuation to note in this story:

My Too	*Capital letters that start sentences*
.	*Full stop at the end of each sentence*
!	*Exclamation mark used to show anger*
...	*Wait and see*

Too much!

Introduction

Have you ever woken up in the morning and felt everything in your life is not quite right?

The child in this story feels that nothing is right in her life. It's either too this... or too that... only one thing in her life is just right.

What do you think this is?

Story written by Gill Munton
Illustrated by Tim Archbold

My cat is too thin ...

Cooee!

My scooter's too slow ...

Toot toot!

My dog is too fat ... Shoo!

My stool is too low ...

My food is too hot ...

Oof!

My drink's too cold ...

My dress is too long ...

My socks are too old ...

My cap is too little ...

My boots are too tight ...

Too this and too that –

but my Mum is *just right*.

Questions to talk about

Re-read the page. Read the question to the children.

FIND IT

✓ *Turn to the page*

✓ *Read the question*

✓ *Find the answer*

Page 8:	FIND IT	*What does she think about the cat?* *What does she think about her scooter?*
Page 9:	FIND IT	*What does she think about her dog?* *What does she think about her stool?*
Page 10:	FIND IT	*What does she think about her food?* *What does she think about her drink?*
Page 11:	FIND IT	*What is too long?* *What are too old?*
Page 12:	FIND IT	*What is too little?* *What are too tight?*
Page 13:	FIND IT	*Who is just right?*